The Turtle Wh... With the C...

retold by Stan Cullimore

illustrated by Sheila Moxley

LONGMAN

This is the story of Yim Sung, a poor Chinese fisherman who had no wife, no money and no food. He lived with his grumpy old mother in a tiny cottage with tiny cherry trees by the sea. They were both very unhappy.

"It's your fault we're hungry, Yim Sung," grumbled his mother. "Why don't you go and catch some fish for us to eat?"

So the next day, Yim Sung went out in his boat to catch the biggest fish he could find. He hoped it would make his mother happy.

But instead of catching a fish when he cast his net into the sea, he caught an enormous turtle.

"Thank goodness," said Yim Sung. "Now we will have lots to eat."

Then he looked at the turtle and saw that it had tears in its big brown eyes.

"You poor thing," said Yim Sung. "I can see that you have troubles of your own. I will not harm you." So he let the turtle go and set sail for home.

But before he could reach the shore, a huge storm came and Yim Sung's boat sank beneath the waves. He found himself in the world at the bottom of the sea, with a beautiful princess.

Yim Sung noticed that her big brown eyes were filled with tears – just like the turtle he had set free.

"Yim Sung, please stay with me," said the Princess. "I am so lonely."

7

Yim Sung agreed to stay with her for three days.

It was lovely. They laughed, they sang and they danced. Yim Sung was *very* happy, but he knew he had to return to his mother (even though she would only tell him off for not catching any fish).

When he thought that three days had passed, Yim Sung asked the Princess if he could leave her world. She agreed and gave him three tiny boxes. "Only open them when you must," she said.

When Yim Sung got back to his mother's cottage he saw that everything had changed. His mother had died and the tiny cherry trees had grown old and withered. He had been away for over a hundred years.

"Now what shall I do?" sobbed
Yim Sung and then he remembered
the three boxes.

He opened the first box and out
fell a crane's feather.

He opened the second and a puff
of white smoke came out.

He opened the third and saw a mirror – a mirror which showed him he had become an old man.

He sighed and said, "I do wish I was back with the Princess."

The next second, the withered old cherry trees burst into blossom, the sun shone and Yim Sung had changed into a beautiful white crane.

A voice called out, "Yim Sung, come down to the sea and dance with me!"

So Yim Sung went to the shore and saw the turtle with the big brown eyes. It was the Princess who had changed her shape again.

The turtle and the crane danced together ... and they are dancing still.